To:

_____

From:

_____

Date:

_____

Message from the Artist/Doodler

For me, doodling is a way for my mind to calm down while I listen to the world around me. In fact, I've learned that I actually retain more information from company meetings and Sunday morning sermons if I'm creating little squiggles, patterns, and figures as I'm listening and learning.

As you work through this doodle journal, I want you to remember this one important key factor: **there is no wrong or right way to doodle!** Give yourself the freedom to get lost in your own thoughts as you reflect on God's promises. After all, if you draw closer to God through doodling in this journal, wouldn't you count that as success? The point is NOT to make perfect doodles; the point is to grow closer to our loving, almighty Father who wants to fill your life with hope and joy.

Creating this journal was a labor of love for me! It is my hope for you to have fun as you doodle through each devotion. As your pencil moves across the pages, I hope you are basking in His presence and listening intently to what God is saying to you through your art. It would be a blessing to know that this process helped you, as much as it helped me, grow in your faith journey.

-Jon Huckeby

THE
DEVOTIONAL
DOODLE
JOURNAL

Behold, I am doing
a new thing.

DaySpring

INK.

HI STAR, WHAT'S YOUR NAME?

Have you ever taken the time to lie down outside at night and gaze up at the heavens? God has created planets, moons, and stars for us to enjoy with our eyes. Scientists now estimate that there are as many stars in the sky as there are grains of sand on all of the beaches in the world! One handful of sand is estimated to have about 10,000 grains. This means there are trillions upon trillions of stars out there! He even has a name for each of them! God is so powerful!

He counts the stars and calls them all
by name. PSALM 147:4 NLT

Fill this page with stars.
Give each one a name.

CRAZY IN LOVE

Our God is crazy in love with us! Isn't it amazing that He even thinks about us? Think about it, the God who created the entire universe, who spoke worlds, stars, fish, and all the animals into existence thinks about us, cares for us, and loves us! What an awesome God He is!

Color, draw,
or doodle in
the details
to the planets.

Even before He made the world,
God loved us and chose us in Christ
to be holy and without fault in His eyes.
EPHESIANS 1:4 NLT

MOST EXCELLENT

In the beginning, God created the heavens and the earth. He made the light, and it was good. He then made strawberries, the stars and the moon, green grass, giant mountains and, oh yes, human beings too. And it was all very good.

His radiance exceeds anything
in earth and sky;
He's built a monument—
His very own people!
PSALM 148:13, 14 The Message

ONE-OF-A-KIND

There are over 7 billion people on planet earth today. It's nearly unfathomable to imagine, but not one of them is alike. Each person is a unique, one-of-a-kind creation, handcrafted by the very hands of God. No one looks alike, talks alike, smiles or laughs alike. Look at your thumbprint. God is so into details that He even individually hand-carved a unique thumbprint for each person. Why did He do that? God is just incredibly into details! He regards each person as a mother regards a newborn baby. He's incredibly proud of each one and head-over-heels in love with His children!

Thank You for making me so wonderfully complex!
Your workmanship is marvelous—and how well I know it.
PSALM 139:14 NLT

LET GOD OUT OF HIS BOX

Everyone has their own opinion on who God is and what He does. But, there is one thing we know for sure: God is more than any of us can imagine. It's easy to believe that He is too busy to help us with the ins-and-outs of our day-to-day life, but the truth is: God is all-knowing, all-powerful, and He is present everywhere at the same time. He is big enough to take care of the details, big or small. He's definitely greater than any box we may put Him in!

Fill in the boxes with challenges or obstacles in your life that God is bigger than.

How great is our Lord!
His power is absolute!
His understanding is
beyond comprehension!
PSALM 147:5 NLT

CALL ME

We have a "direct line" to the King of kings and the Lord of lords, the awesome Most High God, Creator of the universe. And you know what? He loves for us to call on Him...He answers us every time. We may not always receive the answers we want, but we can always have hope, knowing that God sees things from an eternal perspective. He is working all things together for our good, and the amazing part is: we can talk to Him about these things anytime we want.

Call to Me and I will answer you and tell you great and incomprehensible things you do not know.
JEREMIAH 33:3 CSB

Design some cell phone covers.

GOOD DAY'S WORK!

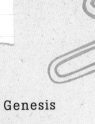

The third day of creation was a busy day for God. Genesis 1:9-13 tells us that God gathered the water together in one place, let dry ground appear, plants, trees and all other vegetation. Not a bad day's work! But how did He do it? How did He gather the waters together? How did He creatively bring into existence all of the types of vegetation in one day? He is incredibly awesome! Isaiah 40:12 says that God measured the waters in the hollow of His hand. God is amazing...and He knows a lot about getting things done!

Draw and color different kinds of trees and plants. Feel free to make them up.

PRAYER REQUEST FROM KING DAVID

King David was inspired by God to ask us to pray for the peace of Jerusalem. What a wonderful prayer to pray! Take a moment to think what it might look like to have total peace—peace for our hearts, homes, churches, and cities. There will be a day when we will stand in total peace of mind with no troubles, worries, or fears. Can you imagine?

Jerusalem needs more details added. Doodle in more windows, brick & rock textures, and add some people...then color.

Pray for the well-being of Jerusalem: "May those who love you be secure; may there be peace within your walls, security within your fortresses." Because of my brothers and friends, I will say, "May peace be in you." Because of the house of the LORD our God, I will pursue your prosperity.

PSALM 122:6-9 CSB

CHEERING YOU ON

Have you ever meditated on that phrase in Scripture that we're "surrounded by a great cloud of witnesses?" Who are those witnesses and why are they watching us?!!! If our spiritual eyes were opened, I think we'd be shocked by the number of cheerleaders we have. Ever been to a long race and see the people cheering the runners on? "You can make it!" "You're doing great!" "You're almost there!" What would you say if you could cheer someone on? Is there someone you know that could use that encouragement today? List them below.

Fill in the clouds with patterns then draw some heads peaking up from behind.

Therefore, since we also have such a large cloud of witnesses surrounding us, let us lay aside every hindrance and the sin that so easily ensnares us. Let us run with endurance the race that lies before us.

HEBREWS 12:1 CSB

LIKE A SEED

Every person on the planet is kind of like a seed. A potential-packed package that needs the right environment to grow into a vibrant, green, leafy masterpiece. Many, many of these seeds stay unplanted, or planted in bad soil. Others stay in their window trays, never reaching their full impact. But there are some that take to the soil and take root. They weather the winters, suck up the springtime rain, share fruit in the summer, and lose leaves in the fall. These seed-people have discovered that the Master Gardener knows what He's doing, pruning shears and all. And for that they will bear fruit the rest of their lives.

These leaves need all the details added in and you're the one for the job. Think veins and color.

For you were continually straying like sheep, but now you have returned to the Shepherd and Guardian of your souls.

I PETER 2:25 NASB

MORE CREATIVITY

Think about the undersea world of God. Sea horses, octopuses, whales, sharks, sawfish, eels, starfish—what an incredible fantasy world that God made real. What about the variety of insects and bugs He made? Crickets, spiders, June bugs, walking sticks, ticks, and chiggers are just a few of the millions of the intricately designed array of insects. Some are so small they are hard to detect with the human eye, yet God handcrafted each one. God has created flowers of every size and color imaginable for our enjoyment. Trees that reach to the sky, waving to their Creator in the breezes, are made for us to lie under and marvel at their greatness. God is incredible!

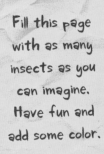

Fill this page with as many insects as you can imagine. Have fun and add some color.

Glorify the LORD with me,
and let us praise His name together.
PSALM 34:3 NCV

God loves you. He's crazy about you. He's your biggest cheerleader. His plans for you are good, and He has a wonderful purpose for your life. He thinks about you more than you think about yourself. Not only does He know how many hairs you have on your head, but He knows how many you lost this morning while brushing it! God thinks you're so special that He didn't make anyone else just like you. You are His unique creation, and He likes what He created in you! Our awesome God cares about the smallest details in your life.

God, Your thoughts are
precious to me.
They are so many!
If I could count them,
they would be more than
all the grains of sand.
PSALM 139:17, 18 NCV

HE HEARS US!

Is that amazing or what?!! The King of kings, Lord of lords, great I AM, Bright and Morning Star, Alpha and Omega, Prince of Peace...hears YOU! What a privilege and honor to be able to have a conversation with Him!

What messages would you text God?
Write them in.

HOPE FOR THE FUTURE

Isn't it great to know God has good plans for us? It would be disturbing to hear "My plans for you are to have a terrible life yet make it to heaven by the skin of your teeth." While we know life is not a bed of roses and we'll all face difficult times (some more than others), we can also be assured that His plans for us are good.

"For I know the plans I have for you," says the LORD. "They are plans for good and not for disaster, to give you a future and a hope."
JEREMIAH 29:11 NLT

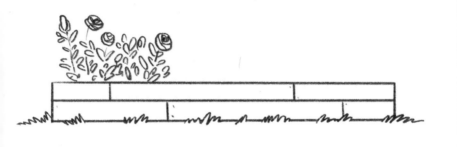

Complete the flower beds. Add more flowers and color.

HOME SWEET HOME

God, in His infinite wisdom, created the family structure. He knew we would need a support base, close people to laugh, share, eat, and even cry with. The old adage, "There's no place like home" is very true, but this truth is even more powerful for a Christian. Our true home, our heavenly home, is unimaginable in its splendor. Leave it to our Big God to create a city with golden streets, crystal seas, gates of pearl, and even a mansion prepared for you! But most of all, we'll get to laugh, eat, share, and spend time with Jesus!

Finish adding the details
to these houses.
Think windows, siding,
bricks, chimneys
solar panels, rock,
shutters, shingles
shrubs, etc..

ere are many rooms in My Father's
use; I would not tell you this if it were
t true. I am going there to prepare a
ace for you. After I go and prepare a
ace for you, I will come back and take
u to be with Me so that you may be
ere I am.   JOHN 14:2-3 NCV

LAUGHING AT GOD

Sarah heard God say that she would have a baby in her old age, and she laughed at the thought! That's right, she laughed at what God said! But it happened! This story should be a great reminder for us that nothing...absolutely nothing is too hard for God. What situation do you know about that seems impossible? Is it the salvation of an atheist? Is it the healing of someone on their deathbed? Impossible situations...not for our awesome God. Then the LORD said to Abraham, "Why did Sarah laugh? Why did she say, 'Can an old woman like me have a baby?' Is anything too hard for the LORD? I will return about this time next year, and Sarah will have a son." GENESIS 18:13-14 NLT

Teeth!! These heads need
teeth, but feel free to add
other stuff if you want.

HE'S ALWAYS RIGHT ON TIME

When the time was right, the sea parted, the walls fell down, the lions went hungry, the sun stood still, the waves were calm, the stone was rolled away, the clouds were parted, the Lord ascended. And when the time is right, the King of kings will return. God is never early and He's never late— He's always right on time and His plan for you is good.

Fill the insides of these clocks with things the Lord has been right on time with in your life.

So let's not get tired of doing what is good. At just the right time we will reap a harvest of blessing if we don't give up.
GALATIANS 6:9 NLT

PRAYER ASSIGNMENTS

Ever feel like you're supposed to be praying for something big...
something way out there? Sometimes we feel compelled to pray
for people we've never met, circumstances we've never faced,
and foreign lands we've never visited. This is what some call
a "prayer burden." God places compassions on our hearts, and
calls us to pray for His people and kingdom. A prayer burden is
usually an unselfish concern and a personal assignment. Are you
willing to take an assignment? Maybe it's time to let Him know
you're willing and able to pray for anything on His agenda today.

God sent His Son into the world not to judge the world,
but to save the world through Him.
JOHN 3:17 NLT

Add more roads, trees, and
houses to finish making the map.

GOOGLE PRAYERS

Here's a new way to pray. Look up a home, neighborhood, city, or country on Google Earth and pray over it. Know someone who's moved recently? Pull up their address. You could even "march around their neighborhood" with your finger on the screen as you pray for their transition, new home, and new friends.

From one man He has made every nationality to live over the whole earth and has determined their appointed times and the boundaries of where they live. He did this so that they might seek God, and perhaps they might reach out and find Him, though He is not far from each one of us.

ACTS 17:26-27 CSB

ASK ANYTHING YOU WANT!

"If you remain in Me and My words remain in you, then you will ask for anything you wish, and you shall have it." JOHN 15:7 GNT

Really? Does Scripture really say that we can ask for anything and have it? Sure it does...but Scripture also qualifies that statement. It says "if" you remain in Christ, "then" you may ask for anything. So what does it mean to "remain in Him?" Are you surrendering yourself to His will on an hourly basis? Just imagine what it would be like to totally abide, believe, trust, savor, rest, and receive Jesus every minute of every day.

Add more grapes to
the bunches then
finish the carrots.
Don't forget
to color.

hose who remain in Me, and I in them, will produce much fruit.
JOHN 15:5 NLT

BIRDS EYE VIEW

Have you ever stopped to think just how many birds exist in the world today? A quick internet search estimates there are 200- to 400-BILLION. Just think about it—if there are about seven billion people in the world, then that would mean there are 30 to 60 birds per person. And, God makes each one of them unique—each wing, beak, feather—all different and beautiful in its own way. Isn't God amazing? Look at the birds. They don't plant or harvest or store food in barns, for your heavenly Father feeds them. And aren't you far more valuable to Him than they are? MATTHEW 6:26 NLT

FOG BE GONE!

George Mueller was a prayer warrior. He was traveling on a ship across the ocean when a great fog descended. After the ship's captain told him it would be impossible to make it to his meeting in time, Mueller asked the captain if they could go inside to pray. Mueller prayed and told the ship's captain that the fog would be gone when they returned to the deck...and it was! The ship's captain was amazed and went on to tell numerous people about it in voyages to come! They also made it to Mueller's meeting on time. Have you seen God do amazing things as the result of your prayers? Maybe it's time to recount His kindnesses to you.

Draw in some boats and ships.

You are the God of great wonders! You demonstrate
Your awesome power among the nations.
PSALM 77:14 NLT

SWEET-SMELLING PRAYERS

Do you have a spot in your home where you store treasured possessions? Perhaps it's a piece of art your child created. Maybe it's a greeting card from someone special. Or it could be your grandmother's Bible. Did you know God has a place like that? Do you know what's in it? YOUR PRAYERS! That's right—they are such a treasure to Him that He keeps them in golden bowls. Now that you know your prayers are treasured possessions of God, is there something special you'd like to say to Him?

Fill the page with more bowls then add patterns, words, or designs to the bowls.

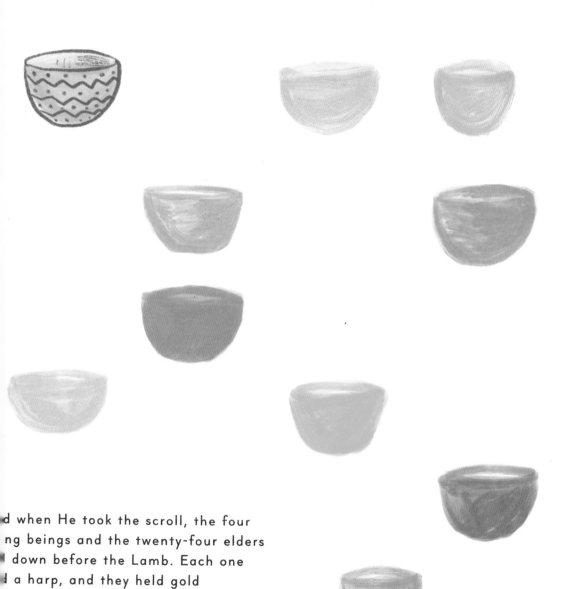

d when He took the scroll, the four
ng beings and the twenty-four elders
 down before the Lamb. Each one
 a harp, and they held gold
ʋls filled with incense, which are
 prayers of God's people.
ʳELATION 5:8 NLT

THANKS AND PRAISE

Each new day is filled with things to be thankful for—from big events such as having another day of life, to small ones such as finding matching socks in the dryer (although sometimes that can seem big!). But in our busyness and struggles, it's easy to forget to give thanks. Sometimes our feelings don't lend to thoughts of gratefulness—it's much easier to dwell on what is wrong rather than what is right. When that happens, the best cure is to start giving thanks about anything—the key is just to start. Give thanks for the first thing that comes to mind—nothing is too small. All gratefulness builds into a big deposit of love for the One who gives us reason to live and praise His name.

Enter His gates with thanksgiving;
go into His courts with praise.
Give thanks to Him and praise His name.
PSALM 100:4 NLT

HE IS FAITHFUL

God's love is before your very eyes. Really, it's all around.
No matter where you are, take a look and start counting His
touches of love. If you're inside, there are walls holding
a roof over your head. Electricity and a place to sit and
rest are part of His provision. If you're outside, you have
the warmth of the sun, birds chirping, and a soft breeze
caressing your face. All of these provisions, plus so much
more, are His ways of loving and showing you He cares
about where you are and the details of your life. He is
faithful right before your very eyes, you just have to look.

GOD'S LOVE (IS) EVERYWHERE

For Your faithful love guides me,
and I live by Your truth.
PSALM 26:3 CSB

RELATIONSHIPS ARE KEY

Have you ever seen a hearse with a U-Haul® trailer behind it? Of course not. Know why? Because we're not taking anything with us when we're called to our heavenly home. Well, wait, there is one thing...the relationships we've developed with other believers. In Christ, those relationships are eternal! When God's people get together, God's Spirit moves powerfully in and through us to accomplish amazing miracles none of us could do on our own. We may have different personalities, looks, and backgrounds, but we still have the same Spirit of God in us that draws us together in a strong way no matter how long it's been since we last spoke.

If we love each other, God lives in us.
1 JOHN 4:12 NLT

Draw stick figures for all your friends & family.
Write their name by each one. Come back to this
page occasionally and pray for each of them.

PRAYER COVERING

Don't you just love the passage about the armor of God? Because of the gift of His mighty armor, we know that we can walk and live every day within the safety of His full protection. In fact, there may be someone out there that needs to be covered in His armor this very moment. They could be on the other side of the world, next door, or in the other room. Remembering to pray for protection over those in danger could make all the difference.

Finally, be strengthened by the Lord and by His vast strength. Put on the full armor of God so that you can stand against the schemes of the devil. EPHESIANS 6:10-11 CSB

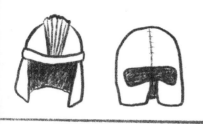

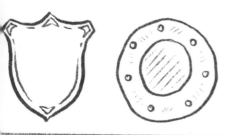

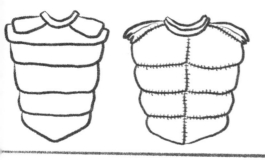

HE REJOICES OVER YOU!

The same God that spoke the world into existence rejoices over you! Is that amazing or what?! You give Him so much joy, in fact, that He starts singing! Yes, He chose you to be in His family, imperfections and all. He chose you for a special purpose. And when you seek Him and carry out that purpose, He has blessings above your imagination in store.

Music!!!
Fill this page
with as many
musicial items
as you can
imagine.
Think
notes, treble
clefs,
instruments,
radios, etc...

he LORD your God is with you; the
ghty One will save you. He will rejoice
r you. You will rest in His love; He
sing and be joyful about you.
HANIAH 3:17 NCV

GOD OF HOPE

Scripture calls our awesome God "the God of hope." And it says if we trust Him, He will fill us with joy and peace...that our hope may overflow, knowing that our ultimate outcome is in His perfect hands. So, the whole idea of seeing a glass "half empty" just doesn't work when you're standing on the one, true Source of genuine hope everlasting. And, as an added bonus, when we trust Him to overflow our glass with hope, we also get the benefits of experiencing His sweet joy and perfect peace.

Now may the God of hope fill you with all joy and peace as you believe
so that you may overflow with hope by the power of the Holy Spirit.
ROMANS 15:13 CSB

Life is crazy busy. Basically we get up, maybe shower, run out the door to work, hurry home, veg for a few hours, and go to bed, to repeat it again the next day. Aaaagh!! This crazy cycle can be exhausting. Yet in the midst of this craziness, God says: "Be still and know that I am God." Wait a minute. Screech on the brakes. What did He say??? Be still??!!!!!!! That's right... be still, talk to Him, then listen...listen very intently...and you just might hear that still, small quiet voice speaking to you.

Add details to the city scene below. We already started a few.
Think windows, leaves, awnings, birds in the sky, people, etc.

Be still, and know that I am God.
PSALM 46:10 KJV

GOD'S HANDS

Remember the old song, *He's got the whole world, in His hands...?* When plans go as scheduled and everything seems to be running on time, it's easy to believe that we are in total control, masterfully planning and executing our lives. But, the truth is, He is in control. He is working in all things, all the time, all around us, everywhere we go. And He is doing it for our good. Isn't that refreshing? Can't you just imagine God's hands holding you? Holding your family? Holding the planet? The entire universe?

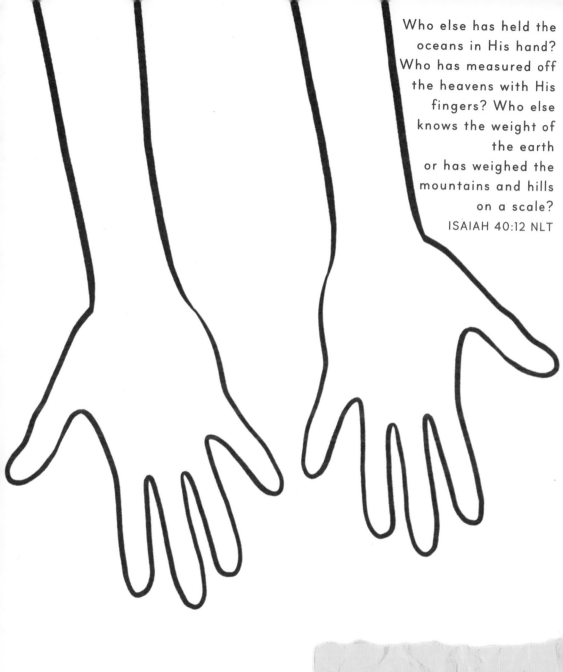

Who else has held the
oceans in His hand?
Who has measured off
the heavens with His
fingers? Who else
knows the weight of
the earth
or has weighed the
mountains and hills
on a scale?
ISAIAH 40:12 NLT

Fill in the hands with the things
you'd like God to help you hold.
Words or drawings.

SHARK DAY!

Sometimes sharks get a bum rap. After all, sharks were created by God. But what comes to mind when you think of sharks? Yep, your brain starts screaming "Danger! Danger!" While hanging out with sharks may not be the best idea, thinking about them as God's creation kind of puts things in perspective. People are sort of that way too. We all have those people that when they come to mind we hear "Avoid! Avoid!" When this happens, maybe it's a good time to lift up a little prayer and ask God to help us see that person (or shark) through His loving eyes instead of our own flawed vision.

God looked over everything He had made;
it was good, so very good!
GENESIS 1:31 The Message

Doodle in details to the shark
shapes. Don't forget the gills!

THE CREATOR IS CREATIVE

There are 7.77 million different types of animals in this world. And, the Bible says all of them were made in one day. Talk about creativity! God carefully crafted, painted, and designed every creature, from the red-and-black dotted ladybug to the long-necked giraffe, the colorful wings of the butterfly to the stubby legs of the rhinoceros. He created cows to produce milk and chickens to produce eggs. And, He breathed life into 7.77 million creatures. In one day. Wow.

Draw some animals that haven't been discovered yet! Then name them all.

Then God said, "Let the earth produce every sort of animal, each producing offspring of the same kind—livestock, small animals that scurry along the ground, and wild animals." And that is what happened.
GENESIS 1:24 NLT

SHINY FISH

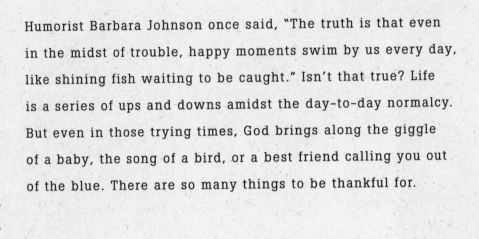

Humorist Barbara Johnson once said, "The truth is that even in the midst of trouble, happy moments swim by us every day, like shining fish waiting to be caught." Isn't that true? Life is a series of ups and downs amidst the day-to-day normalcy. But even in those trying times, God brings along the giggle of a baby, the song of a bird, or a best friend calling you out of the blue. There are so many things to be thankful for.

Finish drawing and coloring in the fish.
Make some of them extra shiny.

May the LORD bless you and protect you.
May the LORD smile on you and be gracious
to you. May the LORD show you His favor
and give you His peace.
NUMBERS 6:24-26 NLT

SINGING IN THE RAIN

Robins are inspiring birds. They're inspiring because, in the spring and summer months, whenever it rains, they will sing—in the rain. Hearing their song in the rain is a good reminder to give thanks and praise to God even when it is raining in life. Not only will your own heart be glad, others will take notice and maybe even start singing too. If robins are mindful enough to sing to their Creator while clouds hover and water falls, we can be as well.

Add more birds singing in the rain.

Then God said, "Let the waters swarm with fish and other life. Let the skies be filled with birds of every kind."
GENESIS 1:20 NLT

WALKING ON WATER

The disciples had rowed nearly all night long and were not making much progress in the storm. They had to be worn out! Then all of a sudden they see this creature, or ghost, or, wait... is that Jesus? Scripture says Jesus came to them walking on water and He wanted to walk past the boat. What? Was Jesus racing the boat? Being the sensitive God-man He is, He realized the disciples were afraid of Him. Don't be afraid guys. It's me! And then the crazy thing about this story is that Peter thinks he can walk out into the crashing waves with Jesus...and he does for a while. Jesus gets in the boat and the wind becomes calm. The disciples knew right then, there's something out-of-this-world amazing about Jesus!!

He saw His followers struggling hard to row the boat,
because the wind was blowing against them. Between three
and six o'clock in the morning, Jesus came to them, walking
on the water, and He wanted to walk past the boat.

MARK 6:48 NCV

Add fish and
other sea life
in the water.

STREETS OF GOLD

The Bible describes heaven as an incredible place. It tells us of pearly gates and streets made of gold—a place where God is on His throne surrounded by a multitude of angels. We're told precious stones adorn the walls of heaven, which is also home to the tree of life and a crystal sea. And, the best part of heaven? The best part of all it is that we will walk with Jesus. We will stand in His presence and experience His pure peace. What a day it will be!

Finish the bricks
on the street
then color it gold.
Add flowers
around
the edges.

e twelve gates were
de of pearls—each
e from a single
rl! And the main
et was pure gold,
lear as glass.
ELATION 21:21 NLT

THE HUNGRY DRYER

Does your dryer ever get hungry? Does it eat your socks? We've all been there—we're sure we put matching socks in the laundry basket, and now there's one mismatched sock in the clean clothes pile. Usually we give it around six months or so before we finally lose hope and throw it in the trash. Have you ever felt like one of those mismatched socks? Ever feel like you don't seem to fit anywhere the way you should? Don't worry. Remember, God created you one-of-a-kind amazing and He has a special place for you...close to His heart. It doesn't feel fun but hang in there. You'll see His plan for your life come together in His perfect timing.

Design your own socks!

"r I know the plans I have for you," says the Lord. "They are
s for good and not for disaster, to give you a future
a hope." JEREMIAH 29:11 NLT

God is the Creator of all the colors in the world. Artists pull inspiration from hues they find in His masterpieces—from the yellow, pink, and orange sunsets to the blue and green ocean and the light brown sand—we create with colors He created for us. And, we've probably only experienced the tip of the iceberg. Many believe there are more colors in heaven—colors we've never seen or could even possibly imagine in our human minds. Amazing, right? Today, let's think about all the colors we get to enjoy on earth, all the different flowers, all the different blooms, every single petal is detailed with amazing, vibrant colors that come from God's breathtaking beauty.

Turn these boxes into flower boxes. Add flowers & then color.

Let's look for wildflowers in bloom, blackberry bushes blossoming white, fruit trees festooned with cascading flowers.
SONG OF SOLOMON 7:12 The Message

WHOOPEE!!!

Isn't it fun to be with a group of family and friends when you hear a funny story and the whole room breaks out into belly laughter? There's no need for the polite little smile, or the fake "ha ha" when you're surrounded by loved ones. In fact, in this space, you are able to completely let loose with uncontrollable laughter, even sometimes to the point of tears. Scripture says we're created in the image and likeness of God. Maybe we don't see a lot of paintings of Jesus laughing or even smiling...but we know He did!!! Won't it be awesome to laugh with Jesus one day?

Finish adding to these happy, laughing faces.

Love from the center of who you are…. Be good friends who love deeply…. Laugh with your happy friends when they're happy.

ROMANS 12:9, 10, 15

The Message

EAT, DRINK, AND BE MERRY

Ever wonder why God made us to require food and water? We sure could save a lot of time, energy, and money if we didn't have to eat or drink. Here's a thought: maybe He knew it would be one of the few times we'd slow down and communicate with one another. We all need personal, supportive, faith-building relationships, and what better way to spur one another along than with a cup of coffee and a blueberry scone.

Have some fun adding designs or patterns to this variety of coffee cups and mugs.

So whether you eat or drink, or whatever you do, do it all for the glory of God.
I CORINTHIANS 10:31 NLT

WALK THIS WAY

When you Google "How many decisions do we make a day?" you won't find a firm source. However, many articles indicate that the average human makes approximately 35,000 decisions a day. Wow! No wonder we're so ready to go to bed at night. Sometimes don't you wish that God would put road signs in front of us saying "Walk this way!" Scriptures, such as Psalm 37:23, assure us that God is constantly guiding us. And not only does He direct us, He cares about every detail of our lives. Is He awesome, or what?

The steps of the godly are directed
by the LORD. He delights in
every detail of their lives

PSALM 37:23 NLT

Create your own shoe tread
patterns on these shapes.

VROOM! VROOM!

What if Jesus would have had a car or a pickup truck to drive around? That would have really attracted attention back in those times!! While He knew vehicles would be invented one day, He also knew being powered by the Holy Spirit was a much better way to travel. When you're walking with the Holy Spirit, you're able to move about fearlessly, with inner peace, abounding joy, and an all-out excitement for life. No car or truck can give you that!

As they walked along they were talking about everything that had happened. As they talked and discussed these things, Jesus Himself suddenly came and began walking with them...Suddenly, their eyes were opened, and they recognized Him. And at that moment He disappeared!

LUKE 24:14-15, 31 NLT

CONSIDER THE LILIES

Consider means to reflect, deliberate, contemplate, ponder, or study. In the Bible, God encourages us to look at the lilies closely. Admire the detail and intricacy He put into creating every petal...then consider {reflect, deliberate, contemplate, ponder} on the fact that He put a whole lot more time into us. That's pretty amazing to think about!

Consider the lilies how they grow: they toil not, they spin not; and yet I say unto you, that Solomon in all his glory was not arrayed like one of these.

LUKE 12:27 KJV

STYLIN'

There are so many cool ways to dress. Fashion really boils down to whatever you like! As you color in all the cool clothes and accessories on the next page, take time to think about the beauty that comes from within you and how that is "precious to God!"

Don't be concerned about the outward beauty of fancy hairstyles, expensive jewelry, or beautiful clothes. You should clothe yourselves instead with the beauty that comes from within, the unfading beauty of a gentle and quiet spirit, which is so precious to God.

I PETER 3:3-4 NLT

THE KINGDOM

Creating a logo is vital for building a brand and successfully marketing a product. BMW, Mercedes, Acura, Infinity—they all have an emblem on the hood and trunk so that, at a glance, you can tell exactly who the maker is, then dream about owning one for yourself. When it comes to living out your faith and being part of building God's Kingdom, the ultimate goal is to live in such a way that, at a glance, others will know you're a Christian, and they'll want to follow you toward God. Bottom line, the Maker wants everyone to dream about life with Him—and for that dream to come true.

Imitate God, therefore, in everything you do,
because you are His dear children.

EPHESIANS 5:1 NLT

HAIR TODAY

God got pretty creative when He created us. Think about all the different colors of hair. How some are straight, some are curly, and some hair is even missing. Did you know God knows how many individual strands of hair you have on your head? Yep, even after you brush it He knows how many just went away. That's just a glimpse of how much He cares for us and loves us!

Not a single sparrow can fall to the ground without your Father knowing it.
And the very hairs on your head are all numbered. So don't be afraid;
you are more valuable to God than a whole flock of sparrows.
MATTHEW 10:29-31 NLT

Fill in the rest of these faces
and draw in the hairstyles.

SWEET TOOTH

The psalmist compares God's Word to honey. But, did you know that the psalmist wasn't surrounded with all the sweets available today? Nope. Candy, chocolate, sodas, donuts, etc.—none of these existed in those times. In fact, honey was most likely the sweetest thing known to mankind. And, on top of that, it was a rare and precious commodity. What if we treated God's Word like that all the time? What if we craved His Word more than we craved chocolate...or honey?

Doodle more candy & sweets.
In-between the doodles write in
some of your favorite Scriptures.

How sweet Your words taste to me; they are sweeter than honey.

PSALM 119:103 NLT

THE CROSS

The cross is probably the most recognizable symbol of Christianity. It was actually used as a means of torture yet we wear it around our neck, use it on buildings, and illustrate Christian literature with it. Why is it so popular? Maybe it's not the actual cross that is attractive, but the work, the sacrifice, the Man who was slain on it for our redemption that has made it the symbol it is today. When you get right down to it, it's all about Jesus!

Fill this page with crosses. Big, little, smooth, rugged, colored, etc. As you do, think about Jesus and all He's done for you!

Never boast about anything except the cross of our Lord Jesus Christ.
GALATIANS 6:14 NLT

STAINED GLASS

Each individual piece of a stained glass window is really not that pretty by itself. But when you combine all the different colored pieces of glass, it becomes beautiful and has a wonderful story to tell. It's kind of like the Body of Christ. Individually we're uniquely created and loved, but when you combine us all together, we become even more beautiful and are a part of the greatest story ever told.

Design some stained glass windows. Make sure you color them afterwards.

We are all one body in Christ, we belong to each other, and each of us needs all the others.
ROMANS 12:5 NLT

HERE KITTY KITTY

There's something calming and soothing about a cat curled up sleeping and purring. It's as if they don't have a care in the world. They've found their "happy place." Our Father likes it when we cast our cares on Him and curl up in His lap and rest. There's no better place to be than spending time with our Heavenly Father.

Apply your special touch to all of these fancy felines.

Give your worries to the LORD, and He will take care of you. He will never let good people down.

PSALM 55:22 NCV

PLANT, WATER, HARVEST

Ever plant a garden? It seems like a long time from when you first plant it until it sprouts out of the ground. And then as you water it, it continues to grow until one day you get a bountiful harvest. That's kind of the way our lives are with God and others. Some people "plant" seeds in our lives, others water, and others harvest...but as the Scripture says, it's God that brings the growth in our lives!

Fill this page with veggies.

NO FURTHER

The discussion God has with Job is classic! God says, "Who shut the doors to keep the sea in when it broke through and was born, when I made the clouds like a coat for the sea and wrapped it in dark clouds, when I put limits on the sea and put its doors and bars in place, when I said to the sea, 'You may come this far, but no farther; this is where your proud waves must stop'?" JOB 38:8–11 NCV

Only God Almighty could make the claims He does. Only God can tell the seas, "Your waves can only come this far and then they have to turn around and go back!" His awesomeness is beyond compare, His majesty is incomprehensible, His power is magnanimous!

With a blue or white pen or marker, add wave lines to the water to create patterns. Add some shells or pebbles to the sand.

CAN YOU IMAGINE?

Did you know that there are reportedly 298,000 different types of plant species? And God created them all in one day. It's true! The Bible says He simply said "Let the land sprout with vegetation," and at that very moment plants, trees, grass— every single root that grows from the ground instantly covered the land. Can you imagine? What a sight to watch, as the Great Artist, in all His power filled the dry ground with all different hues of greens, reds, yellows and the many, many different colors God gave us to enjoy. He filled the hills with green pines, the rainforest with banana trees, the deserts with cacti, and the beach with palm trees. He had a purpose for every single beautiful bloom He created—let's remember to praise Him for the beauty He surrounds us with each day.

Doodle some plants & trees
that haven't been discovered yet.
Add some fruits and name them.

Then God said, "Let the land sprout with vegetation—
every sort of seed-bearing plant, and trees that grow
seed-bearing fruit. These seeds will then produce
the kinds of plants and trees from which they came."
And that is what happened.

GENESIS 1:11 NLT

TIME OUT!

Sometimes we just need to call a time out from life. Things get hectic, crazy, and we just can't keep up with everything. Home life, work life, school, oil changes, lawns to mow, dishes to wash...TIME OUT! Jesus knew we'd have times like this. After a busy day of healing, preaching, feeding the 5,000, etc. He would often get away for some one-on-one time with the Father. Time outs are ok!

Redesign the shirts that Refs wear. Come up with your own new colors and patterns.

Crowds of people were coming and going so that Jesus and His followers did not even have time to eat. He said to them, "Come away by yourselves, and we will go to a lonely place to get some rest." MARK 6:31 NCV

FRESH N BREEZY

Years ago people used to hang their clothes out on a clothesline to dry. A few brave souls probably still do. The best part about it was that your clothes just always smelled so good! In Scripture we're exhorted to follow Christ and to serve and sacrifice ourselves for others. When we do this the Bible says it's a pleasing aroma to God. Maybe it even smells fresh and breezy.

Imitate God, therefore, in everything you do, because you are His dear children.
Live a life filled with love, following the example of Christ.
He loved us and offered Himself as a sacrifice for us,
a pleasing aroma to God.

EPHESIANS 5:1-2 NLT

Doodle more clothes on the lines
then color them in.

AMBIDEXTROUS

Ever wonder if God meant for people to be ambidextrous? Perhaps not. It's interesting, though, that most folks have a dominant right hand or left hand. The Bible says we're made in His image and likeness. God's gotta be ambidextrous! To get everything done that He did during creation...He had to have both hands going at once!!

Left Hand		Right Hand

God created human beings in His image. In the image of God He created them.
GENESIS 1:27 NCV

IT'S A MIRACLE

Jesus' first miracle was turning water into wine at a wedding reception. In those times, it was a great embarrassment for the host to run out of wine. So, Mary, Jesus' mother, asked her Son to help the hosts when their supply started running low. And, Jesus did just that. He saved the newlyweds and their families from what could have been an embarrassing situation. What can we learn from this? Jesus is paying attention to the details. His first miracle wasn't a life-or-death situation, crisis or emergency, yet Jesus showed concern enough to act. Jesus constantly shows He cares about the details of our lives. May we not miss seeing His acts of love.

Put your pen down and just start drawing all over the page. You can't lift your pen off the page though! After you fill the page in, color in all the circles and ovals you've created!

When he tasted it, the water had become wine. He did not know where the wine came from, but the servants who had brought the water knew.

JOHN 2:9 NCV

NAMES OF GOD

Scripture is full of different names of God. Many of them describe an attribute or character of God. Names like Christ, Savior, Lord, Good Shepherd, and Light of the World are a few from the New Testament. From the Old Testament there are many Hebrew names for God. Yahweh, Jehovah Rapha, Jehovah Shalom, etc. Each one has a specific meaning and can turn into a great Bible study!

God raised Him up to heights of heaven and gave
Him a name that is above every other name.
PHILIPPIANS 2:9 NLT

Write as many names of God you can think of or find.
Fill the space between the words with fun patterns.

PURE DELIGHT

Inhaling a deep breath after a fresh spring rain, listening to morning birds burst forth in praise, being still and relishing quiet time with God—all of these experiences bring moments of delight in the Lord. And as you spend more and more time with Him, He plants seeds of desire for His purposes for you. As you give Him your heart, He sings back to yours, calling you to fulfill the exact purpose He's created you for—and it will be a masterpiece.

Draw hearts all over the page. Big hearts, little hearts, colored hearts, patterned hearts. Between all the hearts write some ideas how you could spend more time with God. Also pray about your heart's desires and write some of those down.

Take delight in the LORD,
and He will give you your heart's desires.
PSALM 37:4 CSB

GOOD FRUIT

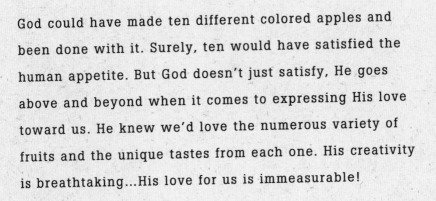

God could have made ten different colored apples and been done with it. Surely, ten would have satisfied the human appetite. But God doesn't just satisfy, He goes above and beyond when it comes to expressing His love toward us. He knew we'd love the numerous variety of fruits and the unique tastes from each one. His creativity is breathtaking...His love for us is immeasurable!

Fill the page with fruit.
Color in the fruit and add
the fruit of the Spirit
names throughout.

But the Holy Spirit produces this kind of fruit in our lives:
love, joy, peace, patience, kindness, goodness, faithfulness.
GALATIANS 5:22 NLT

IMPOSSIBLE?

Don't you just love that God says nothing is impossible for Him? Period. End of discussion. No exceptions. He didn't say, "Well, I can do most things but don't come to me on Tuesdays, Thursdays, or Sundays because I'll probably be napping." No, God tells us that He is on call 24 hours a day, seven days a week and nothing, absolutely nothing is too hard for Him.

I am the LORD, the God of every person on the earth. Nothing is impossible for Me.
JEREMIAH 32:27 NCV

Doodle impossible things.

HERE'S THE CHURCH
HERE'S THE STEEPLE

For centuries, people have constructed places to worship God. In Scripture, the tabernacle was the first place. Later, Solomon built an amazing temple for God in Jerusalem. Today, there are many different types of facilities where God is worshipped. While it's perfectly normal to be picky about where we worship, let's remember that God is more concerned with our hearts toward him. He should be our focus. He should be the One we seek. Our heart of worship should be for Him and nothing or no one else!

Now to Him who is able to do exceedingly abundantly above all that we ask or think, according to the power that works in us, to Him be glory in the church by Christ Jesus to all generations, forever and ever. Amen.

EPHESIANS 3:20-21 NKJV

SIGNS EVERYWHERE!

Jesus speaks a lot about "signs of the times." He indicates that we'll know when His return is soon by different signs on earth. It says no one knows the time but it indicates that we'll know the season. Sounds like a cool time to be alive on planet earth. God's got good things ahead for us!

Make up your own signs.

He told them, "You have a saying that goes, 'Red sky at night, sailor's delight; red sky at morning, sailors take warning.' You find it easy enough to forecast the weather—why can't you read the signs of the times?" MATTHEW 16:2-3 The Message

SKY RIDER

The psalmist writes that God "rides across the ancient skies." Have you ever wondered what He rides? Some might imagine the biggest, baddest motorcycle they can dream up. Others might imagine some sort of giant surfboard. Perhaps it's a hovercraft or some high speed jet. More than likely He's probably just flying/riding the winds across the sky. However He does it, it's really going to be awesome one day to see Him in action.

Color the sky in-between the clouds and write things in the word bubbles that God could be saying as He rides across the sky.

Praise the One who rides across the ancient skies; listen as He speaks with a mighty voice.

PSALM 68:33 CEV

CREATED TO CREATE

Everyone is creative. Whether you are an accountant organizing spread sheets, a gardener digging in the dirt, or a brilliant artist painting portraits, you have creative juices running hot through your veins. How do we know this? Because God is the ultimate creator, and He hardwired creativity into our DNA when He made us in His image. Those creative juices you have come straight from Him. Can you imagine Him creating all the animals? From the killer whale and the monarch butterfly to the water buffalo and the tree frog, God created each one unique and beautiful. What creative gifts has God passed on to you? Maybe it's time to stop denying your creative skills and instead, use them to bring glory to the greatest Creator of all.

We all know the buffalo check. Fill in some of these other animals and show what their check would look like!

DINOSAURS

The word dinosaur actually does not appear in Scripture. Perhaps the words "dragon," or "land monster" refers to what we know as dinosaurs. We do know these huge reptiles lived on our planet and walked this earth and that God obviously created them. But why? And, what happened to them? While we don't know for sure, it's amazing to imagine these magnificent creatures roaming the earth. God created a fascinating world, and with it, He continues to remind us of how truly BIG He is—dragons, land monsters, and dinosaurs to humans, cars, and cell phones. He is over all of it.

Try drawing the dinosaurs shown.
Color them in or create patterns on them.

Everything God created is good.

I TIMOTHY 4:4 The Message

BEAUTY ALL AROUND

God really spoiled us. Did He really need to create thousands of types of flowers? A simple dozen or hundred would have done. And trees, why so much variety? Ten different kinds could have been enough. And all the clouds? What if just one cloud floated by each day and either it rained or it didn't? He didn't want us to get bored, did He? Take time today to notice all the details He created just for you!

Yes, there will be an abundance of flowers and singing and joy!...
There the LORD will display His glory, the splendor of our God.

ISAIAH 35:2 NLT

WHAT A DAY

Many of us rarely think about the day Jesus will return. But, this is a day that is really, really going to happen. God will be shouting, trumpets will be sounding, people will be reunited with Jesus. And, the kicker of the whole day is that we will get to stay in the presence of the Lord FOREVER! What an awesome thought!

For the Lord Himself will come down from heaven with a commanding
shout, with the voice of the archangel, and with
the trumpet call of God.... Then we will be with the Lord forever.
I THESSALONIANS 4:16, 17 NLT

Doodle flying
people all over
this page.

SPIDER WEBS

Have you ever looked closely at a spider's web...the intricacy, the detail, the amazing preciseness of each little web strand? They can be truly amazing works of art. God imagined this tiny little creature and gave it the ability to capture its food this way. Another example of God's incomprehensible creativity.

Draw spider webs
all over the page.
You may even
want to try
to make a
word in them.

The spider skillfully grasps with its hands, and it is in kings' palaces.

PROVERBS 30:28 NKJV

GOD OF HOPE

God gives us so many good things. He fills us with joy
and peace. There aren't too many gifts better than those
two! God is always going above and beyond any sort
of basic creativity. He gives gifts that are better than
we need or deserve. What an awesome God He is!

I pray that the God who gives hope will fill you
with much joy and peace while you trust in Him.
Then your hope will overflow by the power of the Holy Spirit.
ROMANS 15:13 NCV

Pick out key words
from the verse above
and draw and decorate
them on the page.

WILDFLOWER

Have you ever rounded a curve in the road to see a field full of wildflowers? Who planted them? Who takes care of them? Who waters them? That would be your amazing heavenly Father who once again loves to surprise you with His creativity. Remember, He doesn't have to do that. In fact, another field full of grass would have sufficed, but He goes above and beyond to share His beauty with us. Thanks, God!

Fill in more wildflowers in the field.

If God cares so wonderfully
for wildflowers...
He will certainly care for you.
MATTHEW 6:30 NLT

Scripture says "Ask, and it will be given to you. Seek, and you will find. Knock, and the door will be opened to you." (MATTHEW 7:7 CSB) Isn't it nice to know that God promises to give us what we need? He doesn't say "ask, and we might get it." He says "ask, and it will" be given to us. We have a loving Father—One who invites us to lift our wants, cares, and concerns to Him so that He can provide what is best for us. All we have to do is trust.

Doors! Draw as many different kinds as you can think of then color them in.

"So I say to you, ask, and it will be given to you. Seek, and you will find. Knock, and the door will be opened to you. For everyone who asks receives, and the one who seeks finds, and to the one who knocks, the door will be opened."

LUKE 11:9-10 CSB

REDWOODS

Did you know redwoods are the tallest trees on earth? There are more than 50 redwood trees that have been documented to be at least 360 feet tall. That's the height of a 36-story building! Redwoods can grow to be 8 to 20 feet in diameter, and scientists believe some of them are more than 2,000 years old. Can you imagine standing underneath one of these beautiful, massive, living creations? Take a moment to imagine the wind whistling through its branches as you stand in awe of how powerful and beautiful and big our Creator is.

A God-shaped life is a flourishing tree.
PROVERBS 11:28 The Message

HOME SWEET HOME

Years ago, B.J. Thomas sang a song entitled *Home Where I Belong*. Part of the lyrics for that song were:

They say that heaven's pretty

And living here is too

But if they said that I would

Have to choose between the two

I'd go home.

It's always been said that there's no place like home. It will be even truer of our heavenly home one day!

_____

_____

_____

_____

_____

_____

_____

_____

_____

_____

_____

_____

As you add details to the houses below, think about the home your Heavenly Father is creating for you.

In My Father's house are many mansions:
if it were not so, I would have told you.
I go to prepare a place for you.
JOHN 14:2 KJV

HOW TO FOLLOW

The Bible has a formula for making your paths go in the right direction. Some people struggle with God's plan for their life. They wonder how they got to where they are, what to do next, and how they should navigate the ups and downs of life. While those are never easy questions, Proverbs does have some direction that may help:

1. Trust God
2. Don't try to figure it out on your own
3. Know and acknowledge God in everything you do
4. God will make your paths straight

Trust in the Lord with all your heart, and do not rely on
your own understanding; in all your ways know Him,
and He will make your paths straight.
PROVERBS 3:5-6 CSB

Draw anything you want...
the only rule is you can only
use straight lines on
the whole page!

POODLE DOODLES

Did you know there are roughly 525 million dogs in the world? There are 340 recognized breeds worldwide, with about half of those living in the United States. The poodle is just one of those breeds. Among poodles, there are three basic sizes:

- Standard
- Miniature
- Toy

The fact that God would create so many different breeds, and then create different sizes of different breeds can only mean that He is a creative God. And, it provides even more evidence of God going above and beyond to bring us more joy.

Finish out
all the details
on the doggies.

God richly gives us everything to enjoy.
I TIMOTHY 6:17 NCV

GOD MADE MONSTERS

According to the Psalmist, God made the sea monster Leviathan to *play* in the ocean. While scholars believe Leviathan might be a crocodile, whale, or maybe even a shark, the point is He created some type of creature to simply *frolic* in the depths of the ocean. God delights in us when we enjoy the beauty that surrounds us. He loves watching life frolic in the goodness that He created. And, just think, if He enjoys watching sea monsters frolic in His creation, how much more does He delight in watching us play around?

Monsters are fun to draw. Start with a basic shape then add eyes, mouth, and all the other parts.
Color all of these when you're done.

Look at the sea, so big and wide, with creatures large and small that cannot be counted. Ships travel over the ocean, and there is the sea monster Leviathan, which You made to play there.
PSALM 104:25-26 NCV

HAIR TODAY...
GONE TOMORROW

The average lifespan in the United States is approximately 80 years. That's 80 trips around the sun, 29,220 days, 701,280 hours, and 42,076,800 minutes. God encourages us to redeem our time on earth wisely. Life is all about building relationships and glorifying God. Are you sharing God's love with those around you? Are you walking with God in all areas of your life, allowing Him to guide you, and praising Him for the many blessings in your life? Take a moment today to think about where you are in your faith journey, and maybe spend a few of those 42 million-plus minutes to doodle around a little.

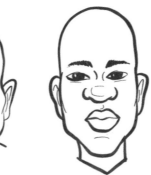

But you do not know what will happen tomorrow! Your life is like a mist. You can see it for a short time, but then it goes away.

JAMES 4:14 NCV

Draw different types of facial hair on these men. As you do this, think about the men in your life and how you can build your relationship with them and glorify God.

YOU ARE PRICELESS

When cleaning out a closet or an attic, a lot of time can be spent thinking about whether an item is worth keeping or if it's time to throw it away. The more value or sentiment the piece has, the better the chance you'll keep it. Otherwise, it goes to the nearest thrift store or the trash. Isn't it wonderful that, when God looks at you, He doesn't compare your worth with someone else's. That's because you are already of the highest quality. To God, you are a keeper...from now to eternity.

Doodle a page
full of trash cans.

GOD IS SOVEREIGN

Sovereign is basically a fancy word that means "holds and exercises supreme authority." In other words, God reigns, God rules, and He has the final say. He is ultimately and fully in control of every aspect of our lives. He is all-powerful, He exists everywhere, and He is all-knowing—which means there is nothing, NOTHING, beyond His awareness or ability. Grasp this truth today, and let the peace, rest, and assurance fill your heart, mind, and soul.

Color in however you want.

Get out the message—GOD Rules! He put the world on a
firm foundation; He treats everyone fair and square.
PSALM 96:10 The Message

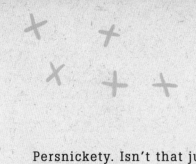

PERSNICKETY

Persnickety. Isn't that just a fun word to say? How about "snickerdoodle" or "kaleidoscope" or "papoose." These words just put a smile on your face. It's as if you can't say them without smiling! There are many people like that in our lives as well—you just can't look at them without getting a smile on your face. It will probably be that way when we see Jesus face to face. We'll probably get the biggest smile on our face and then run into His arms!

Doodle some strange things to go along with some
strange and funny-sounding words.
Name the two below then create more of your own.
Here are a few more words: Bumfuzzle, Snollygoster, Gubbins,
Taradiddle, Widdershins, Collywobbles, Xertz and Bibble.

He and the Lamb will be seated there on their
thrones, and its people will worship God
and will see Him face to face. God's name will be
written on the foreheads of the people.
REVELATION 22:3-4 CEV

PRAYER POWER

No ocean can hold it back.

No river can overtake it.

No whirlwind can go faster.

No army can defeat it.

No law can stop it.

No distance can slow it.

No disease can cripple it.

No force on earth is more powerful

or effective than the power of prayer.

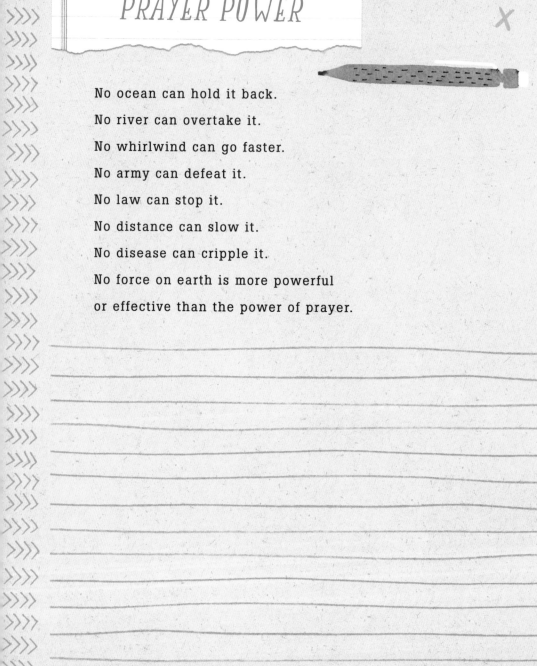

Finish adding color to the planet and the words. Put an X on
the places you want to specifically pray for.
Write your prayers around the earth.

And when he took the scroll, the four living beings and the twenty-four
elders fell down before the Lamb. Each one had a harp, and they held
gold bowls filled with incense, which are the prayers of God's people.

REVELATION 5:8 NLT

FOUR SEASONS

Winter, spring, summer, and fall...the Lord God designed them all. Would people have even known or cared if it just stayed spring all year? Sure, there are some locations where the weather stays the same year round, but for much of the world, God created the four seasons. Why? We can't say for sure, but maybe because He knew we are created in His image, so He knew we would love the variety as much as He does.

He spreads snow like a white fleece, He scatters frost like ashes,
He broadcasts hail like birdseed—who can survive
His winter? Then He gives the command and it all melts; He breathes
on winter—suddenly it's spring! PSALM 147:16-18 The Message

One tree, four seasons. Name, color, and add
ground details to represent the correct season.

PRIZEWINNER

Kids learn a lot about life through sports. Being on a team teaches them how to win and lose gracefully, persevere when the going gets tough, and to keep their eyes on the ball. All of these lessons prepare them for life as well. The race God has placed in front of us will, no doubt, include winning and losing, getting back up when we fall down, and learning to focus on God during the hard moments. While life is filled with ups and downs, we never know how God is going to use the lessons we learn today to prepare us for what comes tomorrow.

Let us run with endurance the race God has set before us. We
do this by keeping our eyes on Jesus, the champion
who initiates and perfects our faith. HEBREWS 12:1, 2 NLT

Fill this page with game
balls. Don't forget to color.

FOOD PANTRY

Jesus feeding the 5,000 is quite a miraculous story. It's even more exciting when you take into consideration that there were actually more than 5,000 people. In fact, there were 5,000 men alone. Meaning, if each of these men had a wife and child with them, that's actually 15,000 people that He fed with five loaves of bread and two fish! Not to mention, they had quite a few leftovers. So, next time we start to limit God, let's try to keep this story in mind. Remember, Jesus can take the little we offer up to Him and turn it into enough to meet our needs—whether it's food, finances, or our faith.

What's in the pantry? You decide and draw in the ingredients and add more labels. Be creative!

Then Andrew, Simon Peter's brother, spoke up. "There's a young boy here with five barley loaves and two fish. But what good is that with this huge crowd?" JOHN 6:8-9 NLT

ROSES ARE RED

Roses are such beautiful creations of God. Did you know there are at least 100 species of roses? Did you know some rose blooms are the size of a grain of rice? Roses have been known as a symbol of love. The next time you stop and smell a rose, think about how intricate God designed it and let it remind you of His great love for you!

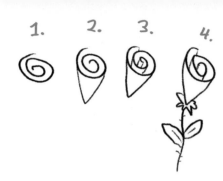

1. 2. 3. 4.

God has made everything beautiful for its own time.
ECCLESIASTES 3:11 NLT

UP, UP AND AWAY

After Jesus rose from the dead, He was seen again on earth by more than 500 people on 12 separate occasions. During His last conversation, the Bible says that Jesus was with His followers when He was carried into heaven "before their very eyes." This wasn't a dream or a vision; they weren't asleep, their eyes weren't closed. They stood there and watched as Jesus began to ascend a little before being covered by a cloud of glory. What a sight! Jesus ascended to sit on the throne of the universe in the presence of God. And, just think—one day we will join Him there.

Jesus led His followers as far as Bethany, and
He raised His hands and blessed them.
While He was blessing them, He was separated from them
and carried into heaven. They worshiped Him and
returned to Jerusalem very happy. They stayed in the Temple
all the time, praising God. LUKE 24:50-53 NCV

Decorate the hot air balloons.

A LIGHT IN THE DARK

Jesus is the light of the world. He is the pillar of fire in the wilderness, providing protection and guidance by His presence. And, while we may be led into dark places, we have the assurance of a Light that will never cease. What a wonderful feeling it is to know that we will never walk in the dark, that the Light of Jesus will always shine inside of us, and that His love for us is stronger than anything we might face!

Jesus spoke to them again: "I am the light of the world. Anyone who follows Me will never walk in the darkness but will have the light of life." JOHN 8:12 CSB

Continue drawing the light bulbs. By each one, write an idea you have about a way you can use your creativity for God's glory.

Z IS FOR ZEBRA

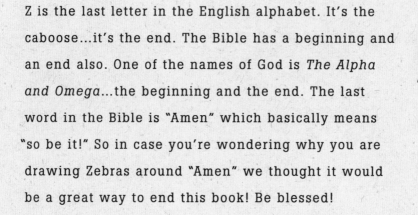

Z is the last letter in the English alphabet. It's the caboose...it's the end. The Bible has a beginning and an end also. One of the names of God is *The Alpha and Omega*...the beginning and the end. The last word in the Bible is "Amen" which basically means "so be it!" So in case you're wondering why you are drawing Zebras around "Amen" we thought it would be a great way to end this book! Be blessed!

Add your kind of stripes or colors to these Zebras!

AMEN!

Jesus, the One who says these things are true, says, "Yes, I am coming soon." Amen. Come, Lord Jesus! The grace of the Lord Jesus be with all.
REVELATION 22:20-21 NCV

The Devotional Doodle Journal
© 2019 DaySpring Cards, Inc. All rights reserved.
First Edition, May 2019

Published by:

P.O. Box 1010
Siloam Springs, AR 72761
dayspring.com

Artwork by: Jon Huckeby
Cover design by: Brady Voss
Written by: Linn Carlson
Printed in China
Prime: 94331
ISBN: 978-1-64454-296-5